This Book Belongs to:

....

Consultant: Fiona Moss, RE Adviser at RE Today Services
Editor: Cathy Jones
Designer: Chris Fraser
Editorial Assistant: Tasha Percy
Managing Editor: Victoria Garrard
Design Manager: Anna Lubecka

Copyright © QED Publishing 2013

First published in the UK in 2013 by
QED Publishing
A Quarto Group company
230 City Road
London EC1V 2TT

www.qed-publishing.co.uk

A catalogue record for this book is available
from the British Library.

ISBN 978 1 78171 170 5

Printed in China

The Last Supper

Written by
Katherine Sully

Illustrated by
Simona Sanfilippo

QED Publishing

It was the Passover holiday. Jesus and his disciples were on their way to Jerusalem. Jesus sent two disciples ahead.

"Find me a young donkey," he told them.
The disciples found a young donkey and
brought it to Jesus.

Hee-haw!

As Jesus rode the donkey into Jerusalem, people came out to greet him. They spread palm leaves in his path and shouted for joy.

Hosanna!

Jesus went to the temple to pray.
All around, people were changing
money and selling things.
Jesus lost his temper.

"This temple is for prayer," Jesus shouted,
"not for taking people's money."
He tipped up the tables.

Crash!

People cheered.
"Hosanna, the king
of the Jews has come
to save all of Jerusalem!"

Hosanna!

When the priests heard people
cheering Jesus, they were afraid.
They thought he was much too
popular and powerful.

"We must get rid of him," the priests decided.
But Jerusalem was crowded for the holiday.
They didn't want any trouble.

"We will wait until the holiday is over,"
they agreed.
"Then we'll get him."

That evening, the disciples sat down to eat. Jesus knew that this would be their last supper together.

He began to wash Peter's feet.

The disciples were surprised. Usually servants wash their master's feet.

"What are you doing?" asked Peter.

"I'm showing you that I am God's servant," Jesus replied. "We must all remember we are God's servants."

While they ate their supper, Jesus said sadly,
"One of you will hand me over to the soldiers."
The disciples were shocked.

"You can't mean me!" they all said.

While they were eating, Jesus picked up some bread.
He thanked God for the bread.

Then he divided it up and shared it with his disciples.

"Eat this," said Jesus. "This is my body."

Then Jesus took a cup of wine. He gave thanks for the wine and then passed it around.

"Drink this," he said.

"This is my blood which is poured to forgive our sins. This is the last drink of wine I will have in this world."

When they had finished their feast,
they went to the Mount of Olives.

"I am in trouble," said Jesus.

"You will all have to keep quiet and out of sight, or you'll be in trouble too."

"I'll never leave you," Peter replied.

"Peter, before the cockerel crows in the morning," Jesus answered, "you will say you don't know me three times."

But Peter wouldn't believe it. "Even if I have to die, I will stick by you," he said.

All the disciples agreed that they would stand up
for Jesus whatever happened.

And while the disciples
went to sleep, Jesus prayed.

Next Steps

Look back through the book to find more to talk about and join in with.

★ Copy the actions. Do the actions with the characters – pretend to ride on a donkey; pretend to eat the bread; pretend to drink the wine.

★ Join in with the rhyme. Pause to encourage joining in with
"Hosanna, the king of the Jews has come
to save all of Jerusalem!"

★ Count twelve. Count the palm leaves, the doves in the temple, the disciples at the Last Supper.

★ Name the colours. What colours are the disciples wearing? Look back to spot the colours on other pages.

★ All shapes and sizes. Look for a big, middle-size and small candles.

★ Listen to the sounds. When you see the word on the page, point and make the sound – Hee-haw! Hosanna! Crash! Gulp!

Now that you've read the story… what do you remember?

★ What animal did Jesus ride into Jerusalem?
★ What did people put on the ground in front of Jesus?
★ Why did Jesus tip over the tables in the temple?
★ What did Jesus say about the bread and wine that he shared?
★ Who is going to hand Jesus over to the soldiers?
★ How does Judas feel when he finds out he is the one who will betray Jesus?

What does the story tell us?
Jesus was loved by the people but feared by the priests.